THE
TRACTOR'S YEAR

Stephen Richmond
& Jonathan Whitlam

**Farming
PRESS**

Front cover
A Case IH 7220 Magnum turns on
the headland of a field with a
Dowdeswell six-furrow plough.

Frontispiece
A Case IH Steyr CS150 round
bales the grass swath which has
been freshly windrowed by the
smaller Case IH CX 80.

Back cover
The Renault 110-54 collects a
hopper load of peas from the
Ploeger pea viner.

First published 1999

Copyright © Stephen Richmond and Jonathan Whitlam

ISBN 0 85236 533 0

A catalogue record for this book is available from the
British Library

Published by Farming Press, Miller Freeman UK Ltd,
Miller Freeman House, Sovereign Way, Tonbridge,
Kent TN9 1RW, UK.

Distributed in North America by Diamond Farm Enterprises,
Box 537, Bailey Settlement Road, Alexandria Bay,
NY 13607, USA.

Origination and printing by TSS Digital,
220-228 Northdown Road, Cliftonville, Margate,
Kent CT9 2RP.

INTRODUCTION

The farmer uses the tractor to do nearly every job on the farm. This book looks at some of the most important work tractors do throughout the year. Tractors can use lots of different pieces of equipment, most of which are attached to the back by means of the three-point linkage (see picture below) or a simple drawbar. Power to drive the equipment is taken from the power take-off (pto) shaft. Many tractors today are also fitted with front linkages and front power take-off shafts so that equipment can be mounted at either end of the tractor.

Side mounted exhaust

Front linkage
Top link

Front linkage arms

Front P.T.O.

Front mudguards

Wing mirrors

Front worklights

Rear P.T.O.

Rear three
point linkage

Diesel tank

This means that the tractor can plough a field, prepare a seedbed, drill or plant a crop, fertilise and spray it, harvest and then cart it away, bale straw and spread animal manure.

The tractor is very special but it is only as good as the equipment that the farmer uses with it. Next time you see a tractor out working in the fields take note of the equipment it is using and see if you can guess what job it is doing.

PLANTING POTATOES

Potatoes are planted from early spring onwards, depending on the variety of potato grown and the weather. Before planting, the land has to be well prepared so that it is stone and clod free. A special piece of equipment called a de-stoner, or stone and clod separator, is used to make a fine, raised seedbed. The potato planter follows behind the de-stoner and leaves the potatoes in ridges.

The de-stoner shown on this page is a 1999 model from Reekie and is called the Reliance. The two Keyag potato planters in the big photograph have large hoppers that hold the seed potatoes. Belts take the potatoes from the hopper to a hole in the soil made by discs. Shares at the back of the machine cover the seed and form ridges of soil, or baulks as they are called. The potatoes grow inside the soil in these baulks.

SPREADING FERTILISER

There are many types of fertiliser spreader. This Bamlett model is of the boom type. The fertiliser is loaded into the machine's hopper. It is then blown down plastic tubes that run along the width of the boom by a fan. The fan is driven by the tractor's power take-off shaft. The fertiliser is then forced out on to a deflector plate that spreads it over the field. In most crops, such as wheat and barley, the tractor and spreader follow tracks across the field that have not been planted. These are called tramlines and were made by the drill when the field was planted. Crops are treated several times during the year with nitrate or other types of fertiliser.

In the spring, winter-sown cereals such as wheat and barley are given a boost with fertilisers, for example nitrate. This speeds up the growth of the young plants and makes the fields – that have looked rather drab and yellow over the winter months – burst into bright green. Fertiliser spreading is properly called top dressing.

FORAGE HARVESTING

The grass is first cut with a mower and left in rows called swaths. A forage harvester, such as this JF FCT 900 model, then picks up the grass from the swath, chops it into small pieces and blows it into a trailer. Some forage harvesters are not pulled by a tractor; they are so big that they have their own cab and engine and are called self-propelled forage harvesters. Sometimes chemicals known as silage additives are added to the grass while it is being harvested in order to improve its quality. Some farmers do not use forage harvesters at all. They bale the grass into large square or round bales which are then wrapped in plastic. Each bale thus becomes its very own tiny clamp of silage.

Cattle farmers grow grass and cut it for silage in late spring and early summer. Silage is made by harvesting the grass and then carting it back to the farm where it is heaped together to form a clamp. A plastic cover is then placed over the silage clamp and weighed down to stop air getting to the grass. The grass then goes through a chemical process which turns it into silage. This is then fed to the cows during the winter.

SPRAYING

Sprayers come in many shapes and sizes. This Landquip sprayer is a trailed type. Water is held in the large tank while the chemical to be used is poured into a small tank at the side of the machine. This is called an induction hopper. The chemical is then added to the water to form the right mixture for spraying. This mixture is then pumped to the booms at the back of the sprayer where it is sprayed out through small jets. This sprayer is also fitted with air sleeve booms that force the chemical down into the crop. Like the fertiliser spreader, the sprayer follows the tramlines up and down the field. Spraying is carried out from spring right through to the autumn.

There are many pests and diseases that can cause problems for the farmer in every crop. Most seed is treated (or dressed) before the farmer plants it to help the plants stay healthy. Even so, crops can still become diseased. Farmers spray their crops with special chemicals if they show any signs of becoming sick. Spraying is also used to kill unwanted weeds as well as tiny insects such as aphids which can ruin the farmer's crop.

HARVESTING WHEAT

The combine harvester, such as this Claas Dominator Mega 208, cuts the corn with a sharp knife positioned at the front. The crop is then lifted up into the machine and the straw is separated from the ears. A large threshing drum then sorts the grain from the chaff – the husky bits that cover each grain of wheat or barley. The grain is then carried to a large tank on the combine where it is stored until the tank is full. An unloading auger then moves the grain from the tank to a trailer. The straw is taken by moving beams called straw walkers to the back of the combine where it falls out ont o the ground in a swath or is chopped into small bits by a straw chopper. Combines can be used to harvest many different crops, such as grass seed, oilseed rape, linseed, rye, oats, flower seeds, peas, beans and even sunflowers.

The farmer's busiest time is the summer when he starts harvesting the wheat and barley. A combine harvester is used to harvest the crop while the tractor and trailer carts the grain back to the farm where it is stored in a barn or large grain bin. Sometimes the grain has to be dried before it can be stored. Large electric or gas driers heat up the grain until it is dry enough for storage. When the wheat is sold by the farmer it is either used to make bread, biscuits and breakfast cereal or for animal feed. Barley is most often used for brewing beer.

BALING STRAW

Straw from the combine is made into bales to be used for animal feed and for winter bedding. The baler follows the swath left by the combine and, depending on the type of baler used, makes small rectangular bales, large round bales or very big square bales. The bales are then carted from the fields and stacked in the farmyard or on fields close by. Grass and hay can also be made into bales by the baler and some farmers even bale pea stalks.

There are many types of round baler. Some, like this Krone KR160, use rollers to form the bale, others use belts and some use a combination of both. The bale is wrapped with twine and then emptied through the rear door of the baler.

MANURE SPREADING

There are two main types of manure spreader: side-spreading or rear-spreading, such as the Richard Western spreader shown here. The manure is loaded into the spreader and then taken to the field. The spreader works by moving the load of manure to the back of the machine on a moving floor. Beaters at the rear of the spreader then chop and spread the manure out over the field so it can be ploughed in later.

When animals such as cows are kept in large buildings for the winter they have to be mucked out regularly. The muck, a mixture of straw and dung, is called manure and is spread on the land before ploughing to help improve the soil and make it richer so that bigger and better crops can be grown. Manure spreading is usually done in the autumn and winter.

HARVESTING POTATOES

Before the potatoes are harvested, the green tops, or haulm, have to be removed. Some farmers spray the potatoes with acid which burns off the tops and also helps to set the skin texture of the potatoes. Other farmers chop up the tops with a haulm pulverisor mounted on a tractor. Potato harvesters can harvest one or two rows at a time, depending on the model used. The potatoes are carried away in trailers for storage, or are collected from the harvester in large pallet boxes and taken straight off the farm. Potatoes are mainly used to make crisps and chips.

This Reekie Cleanflow 2000 harvester lifts two rows of potatoes at a time, carries them from the ground and through a series of belts and roller tables which remove soil and stones. People stand on a platform at the back of the harvester to remove any pieces of rubbish the machine might have missed and also any rotten potatoes. An unloading elevator then takes the crop into a trailer to be carted away. A Standen pulverisor mounted on the front of the tractor chops up the tops.

PLOUGHING

By far the most popular type of mouldboard plough is the reversible plough. The tractor pulls the plough across the field as it turns over the soil with one set of mouldboards in the soil. When one end of the field is reached the tractor raises the plough and turns it over hydraulically so that the other set of mouldboards is in the soil as the tractor makes its way back across the field. Sometimes another piece of equipment, called a furrow press, is attached to the plough. This means that the field can be drilled straight after ploughing because the press breaks down the clods. This Dowdeswell five-furrow plough is fitted with a different type of clod breaker to the furrow press, which is called a furrow cracker.

In the autumn, after the fields have been harvested, ploughing begins. Ploughs come in many sizes, from single-furrow models to massive 14-furrow machines. Ploughs turn over the soil to start preparing the land for the planting of the next crop. Most ploughs use a curved mouldboard to move the soil but other types, such as disc and square ploughs are also used occasionally.

DRILLING

Some drills are mounted on top of power harrows or cultivators so that they can follow behind the plough. This Accord drill is mounted on a Maschio power harrow that breaks up the clods and firms a seedbed. Air blows the seed from the front hopper through a tube and then down through a series of smaller pipes to the coulters that place the seed in the ground. This tractor-mounted drill and power harrow combination is 6m wide. Some really large trailed cultivator drills have huge hoppers and cover ground up to 8m wide.

Barley and wheat are most often planted in the autumn and winter. Many different types of drill are used to plant these crops and a fine, level seedbed is needed. Drills open slits in the ground, place the seed inside and then cover them with soil so that they are ready to grow for next year's harvest.

**To find out more about farm
machinery contact:**

Farming Press,
Miller Freeman UK Ltd,
Miller Freeman House,
Sovereign Way,
Tonbridge,
Kent TN9 1RW, UK.

Email: farmingpress@unmf.com
Website: http://www.farmgate.co.uk